HAPPY BIRTHDAY!

I

Happy birthday! You're finally

____.

2

On the day you were born,
the world became a more

____

place.

3

I hope your birthday's full of

____

and

______________________________.

4

This year, you should totally start

______________________________________.

5

Please don't ever stop

____.

6

When you blow out the candles,
you should wish for

______________________________________.

7

If money were no object,
I'd give you

____.

8

You're not getting older,
you're getting

____.

9

“ ______________________________ ”

should be the title of your autobiography.

10

I believe the world needs
your amazing

____.

II

I am so

____

that we're

______________________________________.

12

On your next birthday,
I'd love to take you to

____.

13

Everyone should

____

like you.

14

I wish

____

could play at your birthday party.

15

I'm so happy that you

____.

16

I love that you used to

______________________________________.

17

Let's party like

____

for your birthday.

18

Your

____

is legendary.

19

I can't wait until we

____.

20

If you were a cake, you'd be

____.

21

It makes me happy when you

____.

22

You need to celebrate with

____.

23

Your birthday piñata should be filled with

____

and

____.

24

I know you really want

____

for your birthday.

25

I still can't believe you

____.

26

It’s always fun to

____

with you.

27

Let's

____

together when we get old.

28

I wish I could get

____

to jump out of a cake for you.

29

If I could sum you up in one word,
it would be

______________________________________.

30

I love how you always

____

on your birthday.

31

I would love to make you

____

for your birthday.

32

We really need to

____

again.

33

If your birthday were a movie,
it would be

"____."

34

You're the best at

_______________________________________.

35

If I could, I'd serve

____

and

____

at your party.

36

I wish we were still

____.

37

It cracks me up when you

____.

38

If I could get

____

to wish you "Happy Birthday,"
I totally would.

39

The whole world should

____

on your birthday.

40

I hope this is the year we get to

____________________________________.

41

Nobody else can

____

like you.

42

Remember the birthday when you

____?

43

We should totally

____

together for your birthday.

44

You deserve to

____

all the time.

45

If I could invite anyone to your birthday party, it'd be

____.

46

You inspire everyone with your

____.

47

Your

____

gets better with age.

48

I'm officially declaring your birthday

____

Day.

49

Now that you're older and wiser, maybe you can tell me your secret for

______________________________________.

50

I hope all your

____

wishes come true.

HAPPY
BIRTHDAY!

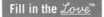

Created, published, and distributed by Knock Knock
1635-B Electric Ave.
Venice, CA 90291
knockknockstuff.com
Knock Knock is a registered trademark of Knock Knock LLC
Fill in the Love is a trademark of Knock Knock LLC

ISBN: 978-160106799-9
UPC: 825703-50087-5

10 9 8 7 6